Theory Paper Grade 6   2013   A

Duration 3 hours

Candidates should answer all FIVE questions.
Write your answers on this paper – no others will be accepted.
Answers must be written clearly and neatly – otherwise marks may be l

RKS

1 Answer ONE section only, (a) or (b).

15

EITHER

(a) Indicate ONE chord at each of the places marked ∗ to accompany the following melody. You may do so by writing roman numerals or any other recognized method of notation between the staves, OR by writing notes on the staves which provide a proper harmonic structure; but use only ONE of these methods.

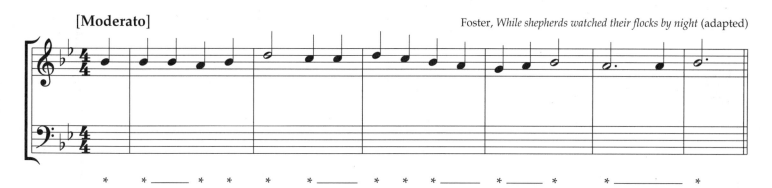

[Moderato]

Foster, *While shepherds watched their flocks by night* (adapted)

OR

(b) Complete the bass line and add a suitable figured bass as necessary, *from the first beat of bar 4*, at the places marked * in this passage. If you wish to use a ⁵₃ chord, leave the space under the asterisk blank, but ⁵₃ chords *must* be shown when used as part of a ⁶₄ ⁵₃ progression or when chromatic alteration is required.

Corelli, Sonata in C, Op. 5 No. 3 (adapted)

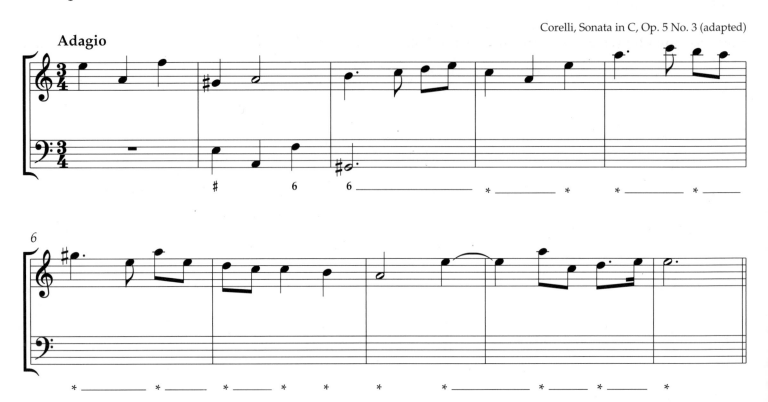

2 Writing for four-part voices (SATB) or keyboard, realize this figured bass. Assume that all chords are ⁵₃ unless otherwise shown.

15

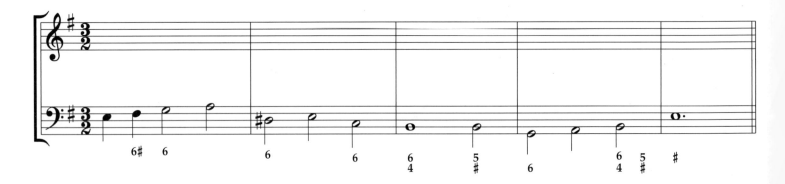

Grade

6

ABRSM

Music Theory Past Papers 2013

ABRSM Grade 6

3-95

3 EITHER

(a) Continue this opening to form a complete melody for unaccompanied violin. It should end with a modulation to the relative minor and should be between eight and ten bars long. Add performance directions as appropriate and write the complete melody on the staves below.

OR

(b) Continue this opening for unaccompanied bassoon to make a complete piece of not less than eight bars in length. You may make any modulation or modulations that you wish, or none if you prefer. Add performance directions as appropriate and write the complete melody on the staves below.

5

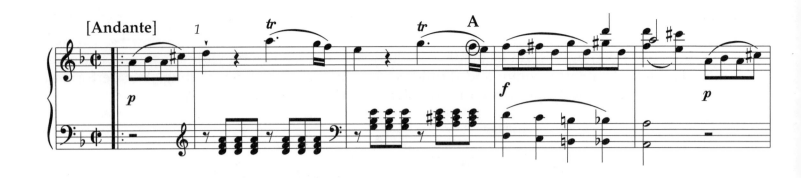

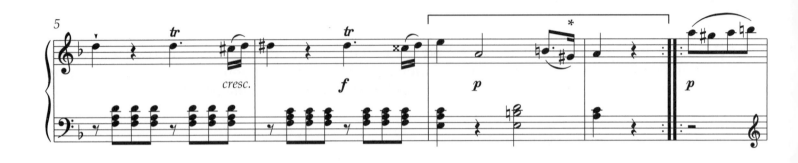

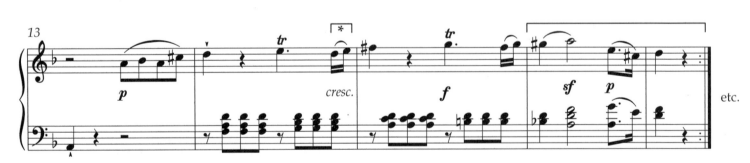

etc.

4 Look at the extract printed opposite, which is from a piano piece, and then answer the questions below.

25

(a) Identify the chords marked ∗ in bars 7 and 14 by writing on the dotted lines below. Use either words or symbols. For each chord, indicate the position, show whether it is major, minor, augmented or diminished, and name the prevailing key.

Bar 7 .... Key .... (4)

Bar 14 .... Key .... (4)

(b) Name one similarity and three differences between bars 7–8 and bars 16–17 (marked ⌐   ⌐).

Similarity .... (1)

Differences 1 .... (1)

2 .... (1)

3 .... (1)

(c) Mark **clearly** on the score, using the appropriate capital letter for identification, one example of each of the following. Also give the bar number(s) of each of your answers. The first answer is given.

In bars 1–10

A an accented passing note in the right-hand part (circle the note concerned). Bar ....2....

B a rising chromatic semitone (augmented unison) in the right-hand part (circle the notes concerned). Bars .... (2)

C a diminished triad in first inversion in the left-hand part (circle the notes concerned). Bar .... (2)

D an imperfect cadence in the tonic key. Bar(s) .... (2)

(d) Write out in full the top right-hand part of bar 15 as you think it should be played.

(3)

(e) Describe fully the bracketed harmonic interval between the right-hand note and the bottom note of the left-hand part in bar 9.

.... (2)

(f) From the list below, underline the name of the most likely composer of this extract and give a reason for your answer.

        J. S. Bach   Verdi   Mozart   Debussy (1)

Reason: .... (1)

5 Look at the extract printed on pages 9–10, which is from Liszt's *Hunnenschlacht* symphonic poem, and then answer the questions below.

25

   (a) Give the meaning of:

      con sord. (e.g. bar 1, first violins) .... (2)

      marc. (*marcato*) (e.g. bar 1, first violins) .... (2)

      ♩ (e.g. bar 1, second violins) .... (2)

      a 2 (e.g. bar 7, flutes) .... (2)

   (b) (i) Write out the parts for first and second horns in bars 1–2 as they would sound at concert pitch and using the given clef.

          (3)

     (ii) Using the blank stave at the foot of page 10, write out the parts for clarinets in bars 5–8 as they would sound at concert pitch. (3)

   (c) Complete the following statements:

     (i) On the first crotchet of bar 2, the lowest-sounding note is played by

       the ...., the ....

       and the .... (3)

     (ii) The harmonic interval sounding between the second bassoon and the second oboe on the

       first crotchet of bar 6 is a(n) .... (2)

     (iii) There is a melodic interval of a diminished 4th in the cello part in bar .... (2)

     (iv) From bar 5 onwards, the second violins
        and violas sound a note in unison in bar(s) .... (2)

   (d) Describe fully how the timpanist is expected to play in bar 8.

      ....

      .... (2)

8

Più mosso (allegro energico assai)

Kleine Flöte

Flöten 1 2

Oboen 1 2

Klarinetten in B 1 2

Fagotte 1 2

Hörner in F 1 2

3 4

Trompeten in C 1 2

Pauken

Più mosso (allegro energico assai)

Violine 1

Violine 2

Bratsche

Violoncello

Kontrabass

(b) (ii)

bars 5–8   Clarinets

Theory Paper Grade 6   2013   B

TOTAL MARKS
100

Duration 3 hours

Candidates should answer all FIVE questions.
Write your answers on this paper – no others will be accepted.
Answers must be written clearly and neatly – otherwise marks may be lost.

1   Answer **ONE** section only, (a) or (b).

15

EITHER

(a) Indicate **ONE** chord at each of the places marked ∗ to accompany the following melody. You may do so by writing roman numerals or any other recognized method of notation between the staves, **OR** by writing notes on the staves which provide a proper harmonic structure; but use only **ONE** of these methods.

OR

(b) Complete the bass line and add a suitable figured bass as necessary, *from the beginning of bar 2*, at the places marked ＊ in this passage. If you wish to use a $\frac{5}{3}$ chord, leave the space under the asterisk blank, but $\frac{5}{3}$ chords *must* be shown when used as part of a $\frac{6}{4}\frac{5}{3}$ progression or when chromatic alteration is required.

[Alla Siciliana]

Handel, Aria from *Semele*, HWV 58 (adapted)

etc.

2   Writing for four-part voices (SATB) or keyboard, realize this figured bass. Assume that all chords are $\frac{5}{3}$ unless otherwise shown.

15

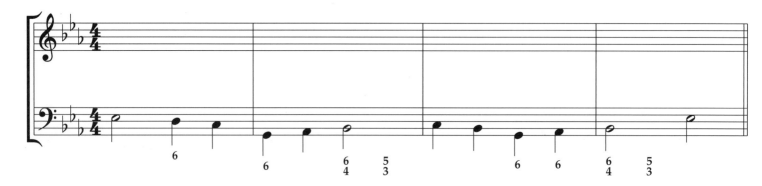

3 EITHER

(a) Continue this opening to form a complete melody for unaccompanied cello. It should end with a modulation to the dominant and should be between eight and ten bars long. Add performance directions as appropriate and write the complete melody on the staves below.

OR

(b) Continue this opening for unaccompanied clarinet to make a complete piece of not less than eight bars in length. You may make any modulation or modulations that you wish, or none if you prefer. Add performance directions as appropriate and write the complete melody on the staves below.

13

4 Look at the extract printed opposite, which is from a song, and then answer the
 questions below.

(a) Give the meaning of **Sehr**. .... (2)

(b) Mark **clearly** on the score, using the appropriate capital letter for identification, one example
 of each of the following. Also give the bar number of each of your answers. The first answer
 is given.

 From bar 9 onwards

 A a harmonic interval of an augmented 4th in
 the right-hand part (circle the notes concerned).   Bar ...14...

 B a dominant 7th chord in root position (V^7a)
 in the subdominant key (circle the notes concerned).   Bar .... (2)

 C a melodic interval of a minor 7th in the
 soprano part (circle the notes concerned).   Bar .... (2)

 D a bar in the piano part where the notes are
 an exact repetition of those in the previous bar.   Bar .... (2)

(c) Identify the chords marked * in bars 7 (shaded) and 11 by writing on the dotted lines below.
 Use either words or symbols. For each chord, indicate the position, show whether it is major,
 minor, augmented or diminished, and name the prevailing key.

 Bar 7 ....   Key .... (4)

 Bar 11 ....   Key .... (4)

(d) Give the full names (e.g. changing note) of the notes of melodic decoration marked **X**, **Y** and **Z**
 in the soprano part of bars 7, 14 and 15:

 X (bar 7)   .... (2)

 Y (bar 14)   .... (2)

 Z (bar 15)   .... (2)

(e) Answer TRUE or FALSE to the following statement:

 In bars 1–12, the soprano part never sounds
 lower than the top line of the right-hand piano part.   .... (2)

(f) From the list below, underline one period during which you think this extract was written.

 1700–1800   1800–1900   1900–2000 (1)

5 Look at the extract printed opposite, which is from the Ballade from Sibelius' *King Kristian II* Suite, and then answer the questions below.

(a) Give the meaning of:

pizz. (e.g. bar 2, double basses)   .... (2)

a 2 (e.g. bar 6, clarinets)   .... (2)

(b) (i)   Write out the part for first clarinet in bars 3–4 as it would sound at concert pitch.

Clarinet 1

(3)

(ii)   Write out the parts for first and second horns in bars 6–7 as they would sound at concert pitch.

Horns 1 2

(3)

(c) Complete the following statements:

(i)   The violas have to play an open string in bar ....   (2)

(ii)   The first note that the second violins and first oboe sound in unison is the note .... in bar ....   (2)

(d) Describe fully the harmonic intervals on the first note of each of the following bars, *sounding* between:

1 bar 4, double basses and bassoons   .... (2)

2 bar 5, cellos and first oboe   .... (2)

3 bar 8, violas and fourth horn   .... (2)

(e) Write out the second bassoon part of bar 8 so that it sounds at the same pitch but using the tenor C clef.

Bassoon 2

(3)

(f) Answer TRUE or FALSE to the following statement:

The first and second bassoons sound a minor 3rd apart throughout bar 9.   .... (2)

25

BLANK PAGE

Theory Paper Grade 6   2013   C

TOTAL MARKS
100

Duration 3 hours

Candidates should answer all FIVE questions.
Write your answers on this paper – no others will be accepted.
Answers must be written clearly and neatly – otherwise marks may be lost.

1   Answer **ONE** section only, (a) or (b).

15

EITHER

(a)   Indicate **ONE** chord at each of the places marked * to accompany the following melody. You may do so by writing roman numerals or any other recognized method of notation between the staves, **OR** by writing notes on the staves which provide a proper harmonic structure; but use only **ONE** of these methods.

[Moderato]

Traditional German carol (adapted)

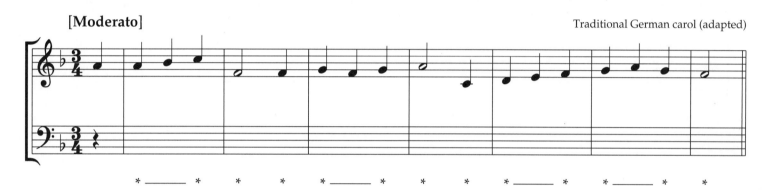

OR

(b) Complete the bass line and add a suitable figured bass as necessary, *from the third beat of bar 3*, at the places marked ∗ in this passage. If you wish to use a ⁵₃ chord, leave the space under the asterisk blank, but ⁵₃ chords *must* be shown when used as part of a ⁶₄ ⁵₃ progression or when chromatic alteration is required.

Allegro

Corelli, Giga from Sonata in G minor, Op. 5 No. 5 (adapted)

2 Writing for four-part voices (SATB) or keyboard, realize this figured bass.
Assume that all chords are ⁵₃ unless otherwise shown.

15

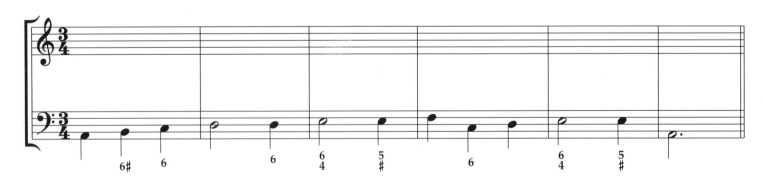

3 EITHER

(a) Continue this opening to form a complete melody for unaccompanied cello. It should end with a modulation to the subdominant and should be between eight and ten bars long. Add performance directions as appropriate and write the complete melody on the staves below.

OR

(b) Continue this opening for unaccompanied oboe to make a complete piece of not less than eight bars in length. You may make any modulation or modulations that you wish, or none if you prefer. Add performance directions as appropriate and write the complete melody on the staves below.

4 Look at the extract printed opposite, which is from Beethoven's Piano Sonata Op. 10 No. 1, and then answer the questions below.

(a) Identify the chords marked * in bars 6 and 17 by writing on the dotted lines below. Use either words or symbols. For each chord, indicate the position, show whether it is major, minor, augmented or diminished, and name the prevailing key.

Bar 6 .... Key .... (4)

Bar 17 .... Key .... (4)

(b) Write out in full the top right-hand part of bar 11 as you think it should be played.

(3)

(c) Name three similarities and one difference between bars 1–2 and bars 9–10.

Similarities 1 .... (1)

2 .... (1)

3 .... (1)

Difference .... (1)

(d) Give the meaning of **Adagio molto.** .... (2)

(e) Mark **clearly** on the score, using the appropriate capital letter for identification, one example of each of the following. Also give the bar number(s) of each of your answers. The first answer is given.

From bar 17 onwards

A an appoggiatura in the right-hand part (circle the note concerned). Bar ...22...

B a harmonic interval of an augmented 2nd in the left-hand part (circle the notes concerned). Bar .... (2)

C two bars that form a descending sequence (not exact) with the previous two bars (mark ⌐ C ⌐ over the bars). Bars .... (2)

D syncopation in the right-hand part. Bar .... (2)

E a chord of the dominant 7th in first inversion (V⁷b) in the tonic key (circle the notes concerned). Bar .... (2)

5 Look at the extract printed opposite, which is from Hindemith's *Symphonische Tänze*, and then answer the questions below. 25

(a) Give the meaning of:

Mässig .... (2)

zus. (zusammen – the same as *a* 2) (bar 1, clarinets) ....

.... (2)

8va - - - - - - - - - - - - - ┐ (bar 11, first violins) .... (2)

(b) (i) Write out the parts for clarinets in bars 6–8 as they would sound at concert pitch.

Clarinets 1 2

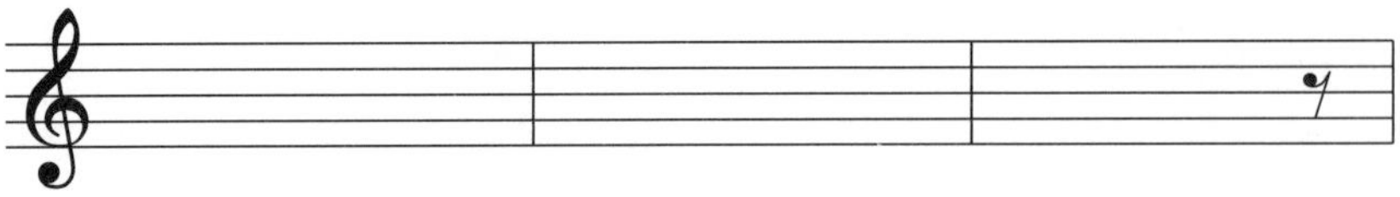

(2)

(ii) Write out the parts for horns in bar 12 as they would sound at concert pitch.

Horns 1 2 3

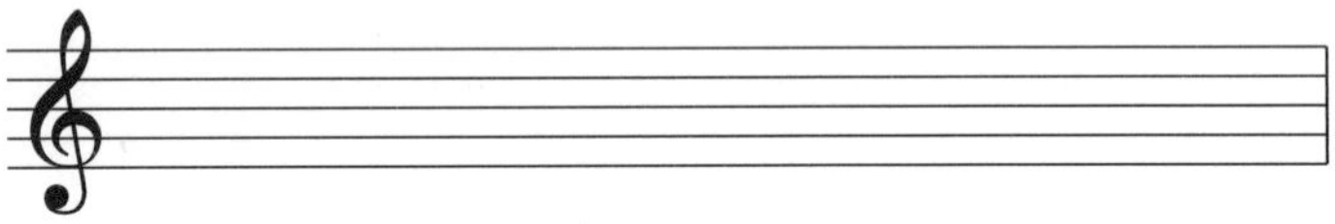

(5)

(c) Mark **clearly** on the score, using the appropriate capital letter for identification, one example of each of the following. Also give the bar number(s) of each of your answers. The first answer is given.

In the string parts

A a place where the first violins and violas sound a note in unison (circle the notes concerned). Bar ....5....

B an indication to use an up-bow. Bar .... (2)

C a place where the violas have to use an open string (circle the note concerned). Bar(s) .... (2)

D a melodic interval of a major 3rd in the viola part (circle the notes concerned). Bar(s) .... (2)

(d) Describe fully the numbered and bracketed harmonic intervals *sounding* between:

1 violas and clarinets, bar 6 .... (2)

2 double basses and horns, bar 8 .... (2)

(e) Complete the following statement:

The lowest-sounding note on the first beat of bar 12 is played by the .... and the .... (2)

BLANK PAGE

Theory Paper Grade 6   2013   S

TOTAL MARKS
100

Duration 3 hours

Candidates should answer all FIVE questions.
Write your answers on this paper – no others will be accepted.
Answers must be written clearly and neatly – otherwise marks may be lost.

1   Answer ONE section only, (a) or (b).

15

EITHER

(a)   Indicate ONE chord at each of the places marked * to accompany the following melody. You may do so by writing roman numerals or any other recognized method of notation between the staves, OR by writing notes on the staves which provide a proper harmonic structure; but use only ONE of these methods.

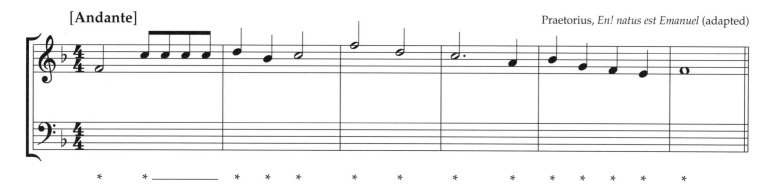

Praetorius, *En! natus est Emanuel* (adapted)

OR

(b) Complete the bass line and add a suitable figured bass as necessary, *from the second beat of bar 2*, at the places marked * in this passage. If you wish to use a ⅗ chord, leave the space under the asterisk blank, but ⅗ chords *must* be shown when used as part of a $^6_4$ $^5_3$ progression or when chromatic alteration is required.

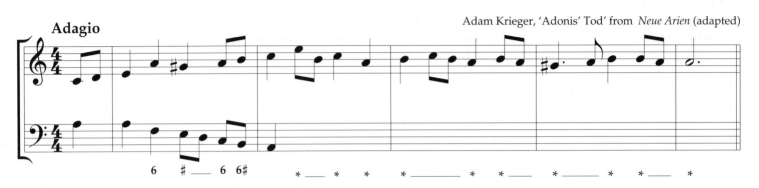

Adam Krieger, 'Adonis' Tod' from *Neue Arien* (adapted)

2 Writing for four-part voices (SATB) or keyboard, realize this figured bass. Assume that all chords are ⅗ unless otherwise shown.

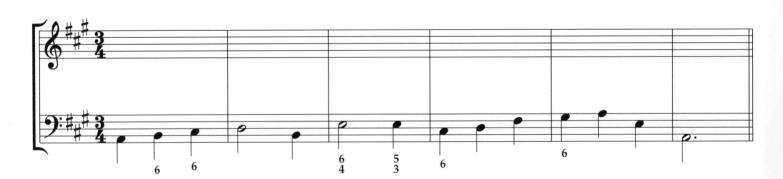

3 EITHER

(a) Continue this opening to form a complete melody for unaccompanied trumpet. It should end with a modulation to the relative major and should be between eight and ten bars long. Add performance directions as appropriate and write the complete melody on the staves below.

OR

(b) Continue this opening for unaccompanied bassoon to make a complete piece of not less than eight bars in length. You may make any modulation or modulations that you wish, or none if you prefer. Add performance directions as appropriate and write the complete melody on the staves below.

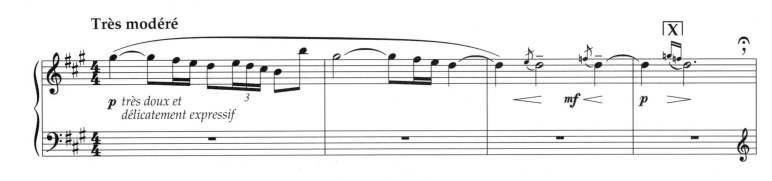

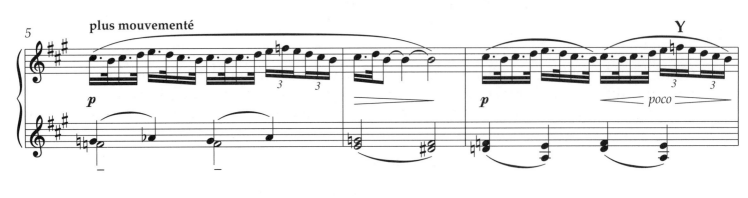

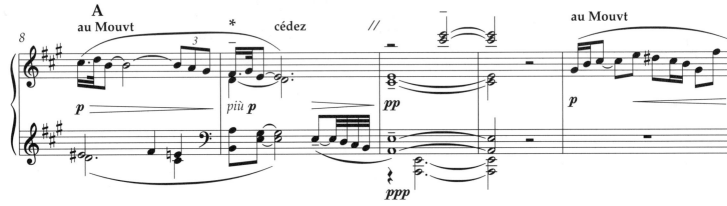

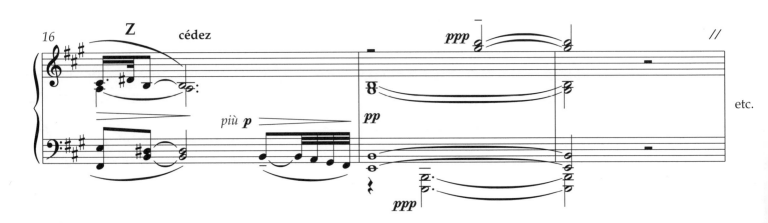

4 Look at the extract printed opposite, which is from a piece for piano, and then answer the questions below.

25

(a) Give the meaning of:

très doux .... (2)

cédez (e.g. bar 9) .... (2)

(b) Identify the chord marked * in bar 9 by writing on the dotted lines below. Use either words or symbols. Indicate the position of the chord, show whether it is major, minor, augmented or diminished, and name the prevailing key.

Chord .... Key .... (4)

(c) Name one similarity and two differences between bar 5 and bar 7.

Similarity .... (1)

Differences   1 .... (1)

2 .... (1)

(d) Mark **clearly** on the score, using the appropriate capital letter for identification, one example of each of the following. Also give the bar number of each of your answers. The first answer is given.

In bars 5–11

A   an instruction to return to the original speed.   Bar ....8....

B   a melodic interval of a major 3rd in
the right-hand part (circle the notes concerned).   Bar .... (2)

C   a harmonic interval of an augmented 2nd in
the left-hand part (circle the notes concerned).   Bar .... (2)

(e) Give the full names of the notes of melodic decoration (e.g. accented passing note) marked **X**, **Y** and **Z** in the right-hand part of bars 4, 7 and 16:

X (bar 4) .... (2)

Y (bar 7) .... (2)

Z (bar 16) .... (2)

(f) Show the phrase structure of the whole extract by drawing
square brackets (⌐————————⌐) over the right-hand part. (3)

(g) From the list below, underline the name of the most likely composer of this extract.

J. S. Bach   Chopin   Mozart   Debussy (1)

5 Look at the extract printed opposite, which is from the first movement of Beethoven's
Symphony No. 8, and then answer the questions below.

(a) Give the meaning of:

   con brio .... (2)

   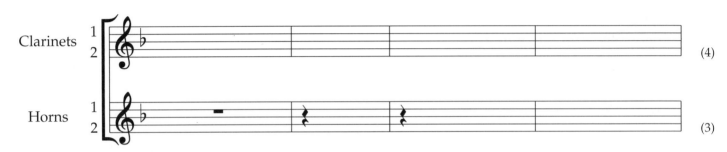 (e.g. bar 1, first violins) .... (2)

   zu 2 (the same as *a 2*) (e.g. bar 2, bassoons) .... (2)

(b) Write out the parts for clarinets and horns in bars 8–11 as they would sound at concert pitch.

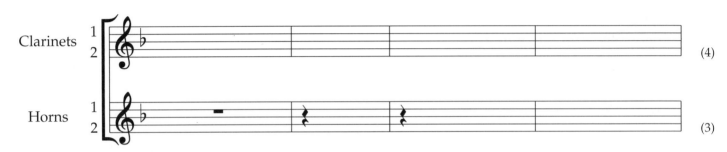

(4)

(3)

(c) Complete the following statements:

   (i)   The first flute and first oboe sound an
         octave apart for four consecutive bars from bar .... to bar .... (2)

   (ii) The instruments sounding in unison with
         the cellos on the third quaver of bar 13 are the .... (2)

   (iii) A string section *not* playing in this extract is the .... section. (2)

   (iv) The chord formed by the notes *sounding* on the final quaver of bar 5 is

         a(n) .... in the key of .... (4)

(d) Answer TRUE or FALSE to the following statement:

   From bar 10 onwards, the first violins always
   sound at a lower pitch than the second violins. .... (2)

33

Music Theory Past Papers 2013

Four separate papers from ABRSM's 2013 Theory exams for Grade 6

- Essential practice material for all ABRSM Theory exam candidates
- Model answers also available

Support material for ABRSM Theory exams

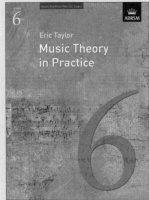

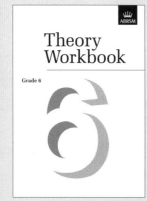
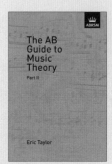

ABRSM is the exam board of the Royal Schools of Music. We are committed to actively supporting high-quality music-making, learning and development throughout the world, and to producing the best possible resources for music teachers and students.

ABRSM
24 Portland Place
London W1B 1LU
United Kingdom

www.abrsm.org

ISBN 978-1-84849-603-3

9 781848 496033

MIX
Paper from
responsible sources
FSC™ C109619

Published by ABRSM (Publishing) Ltd, a wholly owned subsidiary of ABRSM
Cover by Kate Benjamin & Andy Potts
Printed in England by Halstan & Co. Ltd, Amersham, Bucks